Private Lumley and the Cake Confus

A CAMBERWICK GREEN STORY

By Richard Mead
Based on a Channel Four Series

sapling

First Published in 1996 by Sapling, an imprint of
Boxtree Ltd, Broadwall House, 21 Broadwall,
London SE1 9PL

10 9 8 7 6 5 4 3 2 1

Designed and illustrated by
Simon Girling & Associates
Printed and bound in Great Britain by
Cambus Litho Ltd, East Kilbride.

ISBN: 0 7522 0367 3

A CIP catalogue entry for this
book is available from
the British Library

Captain Snort was inspecting the soldier-boys at Pippin Fort. He was very pleased with all of them - except for Private Lumley. Whenever the soldier-boys were ordered to turn right, Private Lumley would turn left. And every time they were told to march to the left, Private Lumley would march off to the right! "What can I do about Lumley?" moaned Captain Snort.

Just then a soldier arrived with a message. Mickey Murphy, the baker, had hurt his hands and needed to rest. One of the soldier-boys was needed to help in his shop.

"Private Lumley," shouted Captain Snort. "After parade, you will go and work at Murphy's Bakery." Poor Private Lumley - he had wanted to have a rest too!

When he got to the Bakery, Mrs Murphy told Lumley what to do. "These cakes on the right can be sold to anyone," she explained. "But the cakes on the left are a special order for Farmer Bell." Then Mrs Murphy put on her hat and coat and left Lumley alone in the shop.

His first customer was Mrs Honeyman. She looked around for a long time before deciding what to buy. "Hmm, doughnuts... meringues... rock buns...," she muttered.

"Oooh, a walnut cake - that's what I'll have."
"It's on the right, so it must be for sale," thought
Lumley. But he was looking at the cakes on his left!

As Mrs. Honeyman walked home, she met Peter Hazel, the postman, and told him about the delicious walnut cake she had bought. It sounded so good he dashed straight off to the Bakery! Then she met Mrs Dingle outside the Post Office.

"Look at my lovely cake," said Mrs. Honeyman, and Mrs. Dingle went to buy one too. Soon, the Bakery was full of customers!

Lumley was selling the last walnut cake to Doctor Mopp when the telephone rang - it was Farmer Bell.

"Mickey Murphy has baked six walnut cakes for my party," he said. "Could you deliver them by half past four, please?"
It was twelve o'clock.
"Your cakes are here on my left," said Lumley, looking to his right. "Everything else is sold, so I'll bring them over right now!".

Lumley loaded the six cake boxes into Mickey's van and drove away from the Bakery. But he wasn't sure

where the Farm was and arrived at Colley's Mill instead! Luckily, Windy Miller was there and Lumley asked for directions.

"Turn right at the bottom of the hill," Windy told him. "Then take the next turning on the left."

But Lumley still looked confused. "So I turn right first," he said, holding up his left hand.
 "Yes - but that's the wrong hand," Windy corrected

him. "Which hand do you write with?"
"My right hand," replied Lumley.
"It's easy then," laughed Windy. "Just remember you write with your right hand - and the one which is left is left!"

Windy then asked Lumley what he was delivering. "Six walnut cakes," said the Private. "Have a look!" But when Windy opened the boxes he found cream sponges and chocolate cakes instead!
"I must have sold Farmer Bell's cakes by mistake," gasped Lumley.
"Come with me," said Windy, kindly. "I can help you."

Windy took Lumley to his cook house.
"It's only one o'clock. You still have time to make some fresh cakes. You'll find cake tins, flour, eggs, milk, sugar, walnuts and butter in here," smiled Windy.

"And you can borrow my cook book too."
Lumley had never made walnut cakes before. He followed the recipe carefully, put his cake mixture in the oven and crossed his fingers for luck.

At half past four Lumley drove Mickey's van into Bell's Farm. Windy went with him, just in case he got lost again!
Lumley parked the van and took the cakes into the farm house.

"They look beautiful," grinned Farmer Bell. "No-one can make a walnut cake better than Mr Murphy!" Lumley and Windy looked at each other and nearly burst out laughing!

When Lumley arrived back at the Bakery, he told Mr Murphy everything. But Farmer Bell had liked his cakes so much, Mickey asked the Private to help him in his kitchen every day! And although Lumley isn't a very good soldier, even Captain Snort agrees he's a brilliant baker!